CONTENTS

GN00865043

Whatever you choose to make first you'll need plenty of packaging, so it's a good idea to start collecting it in advance. Ask people to save things for you instead of throwing them away.

You can flatten cardboard boxes and cereal packets to save space. Rinse plastic bottles and leave them to dry. Prepare an area to work in and have lots of old newspapers handy if you are using glue and paints.

1

HOW TO MAKE YOUR OWN PLANET EARTH

The world didn't always look as it does today. Once, there was just one piece of land. Over millions of years this huge mass, called Pangaea, split apart to form Laurasia and Gondwana. It continued to break up and is still doing so today. If you look on an atlas you can see which countries might once have been joined together.

YOU'LL NEED:

Large round balloon, old magazines and newspapers, paper paste (see inside front cover for instructions), plastic mixing bowl, PVA glue, paints and brushes, string, coathanger.

Animals could walk across the land before it split up.

ASIA

NORTH AMERICA

EUROPE

SOUTH AMERICA

AFRICA

ARABIA

INDIA

AUSTRALIA

ANTARCTICA

33 million years ago, palm trees grew in Antarctica.

1 Mix up some paper paste. Blow up the balloon and tie the end with string.

2 Tear the paper into small strips. Make one pile of black and white and one of coloured strips.

3 Dip the strips in the paste and cover the balloon.

4 Use black and white strips for one layer and coloured for the next. This will keep the thickness even.

5 You'll need about 10 layers for a good strong Earth's crust. Hang up to dry.

6 Tear some more newsprint into small pieces and mix them with the paste into a pulp. Use this to mould islands, mountains and volcanoes.

7 Hang up to dry overnight. Paint in forests and oceans, rivers and icebergs. Finish off with PVA diluted 1:3 to make it bright and waterproof.

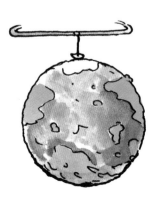

HOW TO FIND FOSSILS

You might not find a rare dinosaur, but fossil hunting is very exciting. Even a small find is rewarding. Look in places like beaches, cliffs, quarries and ploughed fields. Some very good ones can be found on gravel paths and drives. So many wonders of the prehistoric past would be lost to us without them.

MARVELLOUS MARY

In 1811 Mary Anning, aged only 12, found the first complete ichthyosaur. She called it her crocodile. A few years later she found a plesiosaur and a pterosaur. She was called 'the cleverest fossilist the world has ever known'.

YOU'LL NEED:

(You may not need all of these.) A strong bag, plastic bags, notebook, pen, crayons, strong thin paper, pencil, masking tape, small trowel or knife, magnifying glass, suitable clothes, old rag, PVA glue, camera.

Nice croccy!

Fossils are formed when water seeps into the hard parts of a living creature that has died. Minerals in the water gradually replace the shape with stone.

 1 Ask a grown-up to go with you. They'll show you safe places and they're handy for carrying heavy bags.

2 Always ask permission if you're going on to privately owned land.

 **3** Look out for: shells, bones, teeth, eggs, plants, wood, footprints and funny-shaped stones. They may be coprolites – fossilized poo, well past its smell-by date!

4 Bag them and tag them. Find their names in a book or on a website, or visit a museum.

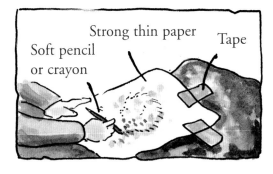

5 Note where you found them. Make a rubbing or take a photo of anything embedded in rock.

6 Once home, soak them in clean water. Clean and dry with a rag. Paint with a coat of PVA glue to protect them and keep them bright.

HOW TO MAKE LAVA LoLLIES

Many millions of years ago, even before there were any oceans, the Earth was full of volcanoes. When they erupted, rocks, so hot they were liquid, shot out. The red hot stream that oozed down the volcano sides, we call lava.

RADIO METRIC DATING AS SOON AS ROCK IS FORMED, IT STARTS TO DECAY (BREAK DOWN) AT A STEADY RATE. MEASURING THIS TELLS US HOW OLD THE ROCK IS.

1 First, wash your hands.

2 Fill about one third of a cone with strawberry sauce.

3 Pack with ice-cream, rounding off the top.

4 Turn over on to plate and cut off the top 3 cm of the cone.

5 Push gently down and watch the lava flow!

Don't eat too many or you might erupt!

HOW TO DRAW-A-SAUR

It's a great shame we can't jump back in time and watch the dinosaurs – from a safe distance, of course. You'd have seen all shapes and sizes. Try these features to make your own monster: frilly necks, spiky tails, horns, humps, sharp claws, and big jaws with an 'I'm going to eat you' smile. But none, it seems, had big, sticky-out ears. I wonder why?

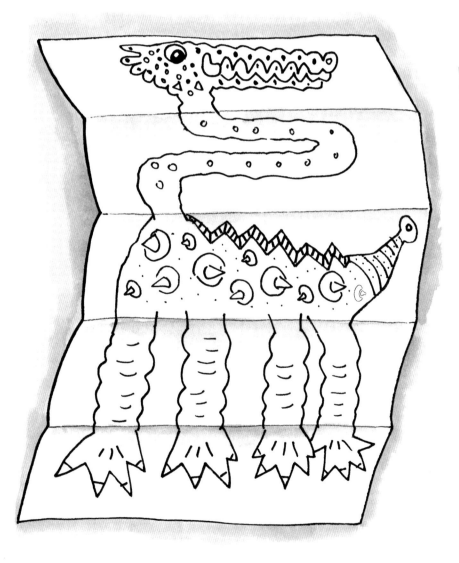

YOU'LL NEED:
Your friends each with an A4 piece of paper, pencils, pens, felt-tips.

NOBODY IS SURE WHAT COLOUR DINOSAURS WERE. THEY MAY HAVE BEEN LIKE TODAY'S REPTILES.

1 Keep your drawings secret and let your imagination go.

2 Draw a dinosaur head. Fold the paper backwards leaving two small lines to show the next person where to continue drawing.

3 Pass it to the person on your left for them to draw a neck. Carry on like this and draw in this order: a head, a neck, a body and tail, legs, feet.

TOP TIP – TOP TIP
Often, dinosaurs are named after the place they are found in or the person who found them, so give yours a suitable name!

4 Then unfold to reveal the latest dinosaur discovery.

HOW TO MAKE A FINGERSAUR

Imagine your finger as the long neck of a plant-eating dinosaur! Make the frill and turn it into a triceratops. Put one on each finger and have a whole dinosaur family.

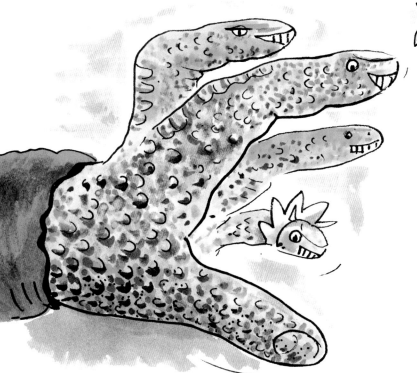

TRICERATOPS MEANS THREE-HORNED FACE.

YOU'LL NEED:
For the dinosaur:
face paints.
For the triceratops:
paper, tracing paper, masking tape, scissors, pencil, paints and brushes or crayons, sticky tape.

Have you got a sore finger?

No, it's a fingersaur!

chomp chomp

DINOSAUR

⭐ **1** Paint your hand and a little face on your index finger.

⭐ **2** With your thumb and middle finger as the legs, pull your sleeve down and let your dinosaur go for a walk.

TRICERATOPS

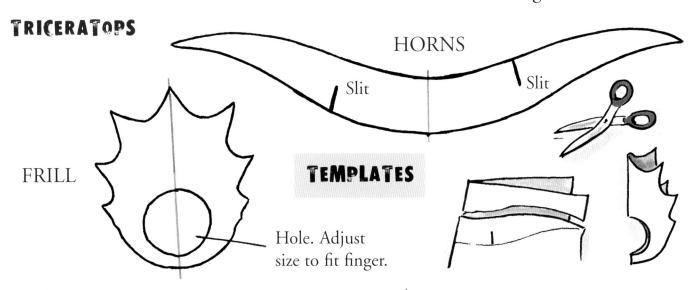

HORNS

Slit

Slit

FRILL

TEMPLATES

Hole. Adjust size to fit finger.

⭐ **1** Copy the templates on to paper (see inside front cover for instructions).

⭐ **2** Cut out. Folding them in half first makes this easier. Colour them in (see page 23).

Tape

⭐ **3** Cut the slits in the horns as shown. Put sticky tape on the back first to stop them tearing. Slot one into the other.

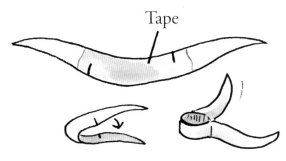

⭐ **4** Put the frill on first, then the horns. Paint an extra horn on your finger face to make a 'tri' ceratops.

11

PREHISTORIC DISCOVERIES

New discoveries are being made all the time. It is surprising how many are made by children!

Rocky Mountains, Canada.
In the Burgess Shale, in the Yoho National Park, 505-million-year-old fossils found. One was of our oldest known ancestors.

Lascaux, France.
Amazing cave paintings found in 1940.

Rio Puerco, Albuquerque, USA.
A three-year-old boy found a fossilized eggshell. It was the oldest evidence of an egg-laying, meat-eating dinosaur.

Dad !

Plaza Huincul, Patagonia.
Argentinasaurus found in the 1990s. The biggest dinosaur discovered so far. It was as big as a herd of elephants.

360-300 MYA	208-146 MYA	65 MYA
First reptiles appeared.	Jurassic period. Many dinosaurs lived.	Many living things died out, including the dinosaurs.

mya stands for million years ago.

THE STONE AGE

Prehistoric people lived in caves and wore animal skins. They used sharp stones called flints as tools and hunted fierce wild beasts like mammoths for food. The children were taught to hunt and collect nuts and berries. Beautiful pictures of animals have been found inside the caves.

MAMMOTHS WERE LIKE VERY HAIRY ELEPHANTS WITH ENORMOUS TUSKS.

HOW TO MAKE A FIERCE POP-UP!

Smilodon, the sabre-tooth tiger, was more like a modern-day lion than a tiger. Too heavy to run for a long time, it waited until its prey came near, then pounced. One bite with those huge fangs and dinner was served.

YOU'LL NEED:
2 sheets of card 24 x 12 cm, pencil, tracing paper, masking tape, scissors, ruler, glue, paints and felt-tips.

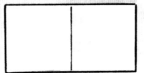

Happy Grrrthday!

1. Divide each piece of card in half and score (see instructions on inside front cover).

2 Copy tiger templates on to one card (see instructions on inside front cover.)

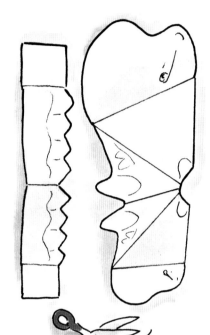

3 Cut round the bold outlines. Score and fold along the blue lines.

4 Colour in your tiger face.

CARD 1 24 x 12 cm

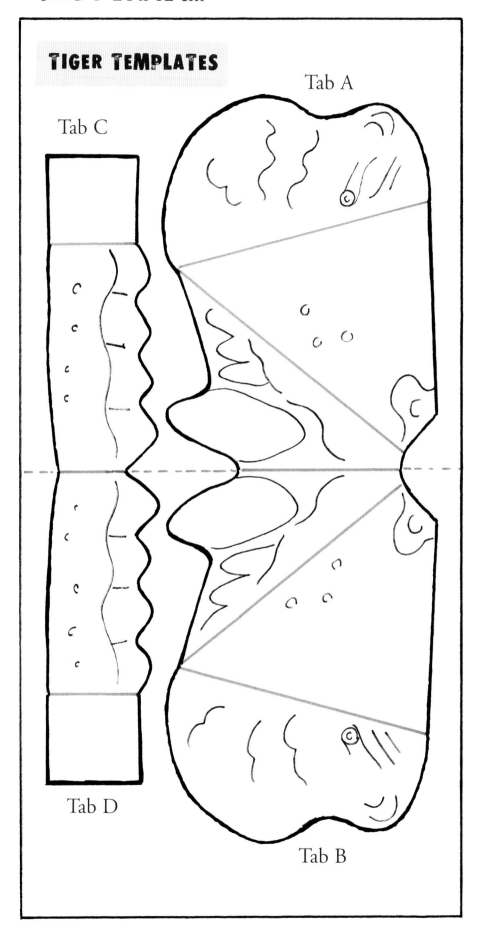

TIGER TEMPLATES

Tab A

Tab C

Tab D

Tab B

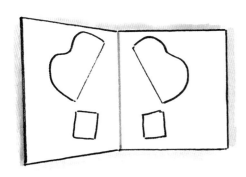

5 Copy the guide templates on to the other card.

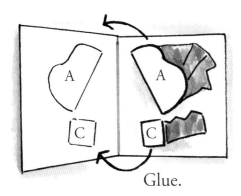

Glue.

6 Stick the back of tabs A, B, and C, D exactly to the shapes A, B and C, D.

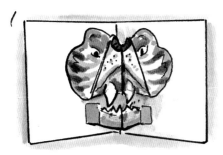

7 Design a front for your card and add a message.

CARD 2 24 x 12 cm

GUIDE TEMPLATES

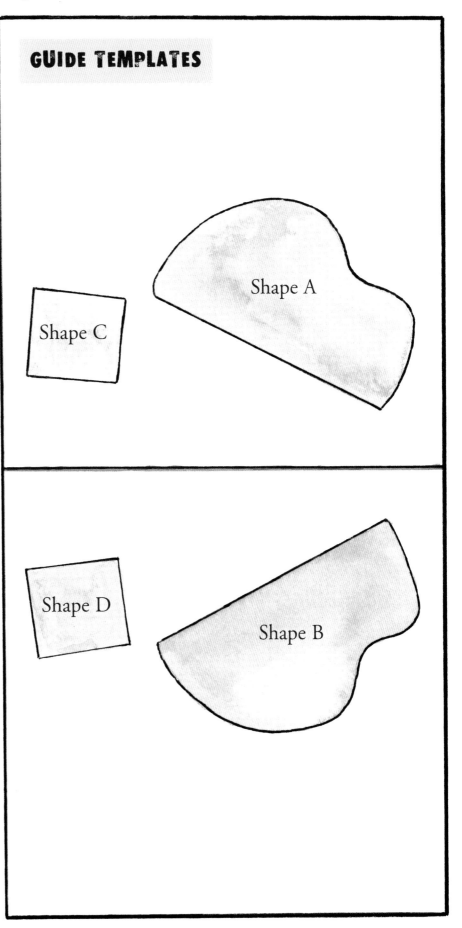

Shape C

Shape A

Shape D

Shape B

HOW TO BE A CAVEMAN

The Neanderthals were Stone Age people who lived in Europe during the last Ice Age between 200,000 and 30,000 years ago. Woolly rhinos roamed the valleys, the sea froze, and knowing how to light a fire became a matter of life or death.

YOU'LL NEED:
3 x 2-litre clear plastic drinks bottles (labels removed), sandpaper/block, scissors, craft knife, marker pen, ruler, acrylic paints and brushes, double-sided tape, glue, 12 x 26 cm bubble plastic.

Everything's been invented already... fire, axes, sabre-tooth tiger trousers...

1   Wash and roughen the bottles' surfaces with sandpaper.

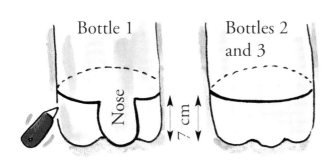

★ **2** Mark as shown and cut. Use a craft knife for the nose on bottle 1.

★ **3** Cut the tops off all bottles and cut down the back. Open them out.

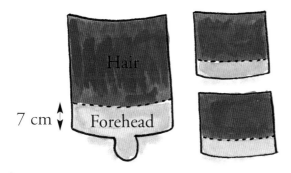

4 On all bottles mark a guide line and paint as shown.

★ **5** When dry, cut narrow strips for hair.

Front view

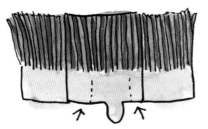

6 Overlap and fix together with double-sided tape.

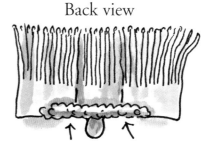

Back view

7 Glue rolled-up bubble plastic inside forehead.

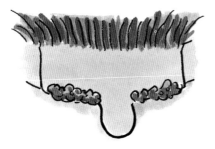

8 Pull some through to the front and paint like eyebrows.

9 Fit to your head. Join at the back with double-sided tape. See if you can invent the wheel.

MONSTER MYSTERIES

Scientists can tell us incredible things about the past, but they don't know everything. There are lots of unexplained mysteries. The world is full of things yet to be discovered and new finds force us to rearrange the jigsaw pieces of the past. Have all the prehistoric creatures died out? Do we know everything that lives on Earth?

CSI CSI CSI CSI CSI

CRYPTO SCIENCE INVESTIGATION

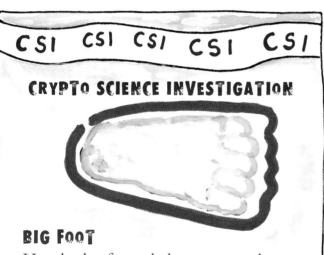

BIG FOOT
Hundreds of people have reported seeing creatures like primitive ape men in North America. They were known to Native Americans as Sasquatch. Footprints have been found and photographed, but we have no absolute proof of Big Foot.

YETI
Also called the Abominable Snowman. Very similar to Big Foot but seen very high up in the mountains in Tibet where few people ever go.

LOCH NESS MONSTER
Many people insist they've seen a strange creature in Loch Ness in Scotland. It's got a long neck and fits the description of a plesiosaur.

ITHOUGHTISAURUS
TOURIST OFFICE

THE LATEST ON THE EARLIEST

In 2002 a fossil was found in China of a flying dinosaur. It was 76 cm long and 120 million years old. It had four wings and was covered with feathers. It may prove a link between dinosaurs and birds.

'IT WAS THIS BIG'

The study of creatures people say they have seen but have no definite proof of is called cryptozoology.

COELACANTHS

More ancient than the dinosaurs, these fish were thought to have died out 80 million years ago. So imagine how amazed scientists were when one was found in fishermen's nets in 1938. They live in very deep water off the coast of South Africa under the close watch of conservationists.

DINOSAUR I.D.

We humans are the newcomers on Earth. Scientists say simple life began 550 million years ago. As the Earth's climate changed, life adapted to take advantage of the new conditions. Dinosaurs thrived wonderfully during three main periods of history: the Triassic (250 to 208 mya), the Jurassic (208 to 146 mya) and the Cretaceous (146 to 65 mya). Then for some reason they just died out ... or did they? See pages 20-21.

TYRANNOSAURUS CRETACEOUS
A truly terrifying dinosaur. Huge head, razor sharp teeth, massive legs and tail. Why the ridiculously short arms? Probably no one dared ask.

PARASAUROLOPHUS CRETACEOUS
A duck-billed dinosaur. Could have made sounds through the bony crest on its head. What sweet music!

STEGOSAURUS JURASSIC
Big plates along its top, spikes on its tail and a tiny little brain the size of a walnut. His mummy still loved him.

PTEROSAUR
CRETACEOUS
Pterosaur is a name given to flying reptiles. The pteranodon was a large pterosaur. It had a 7-metre wingspan and a body the size of a goose.

CETIOSAURUS JURASSIC
Unbelievably huge. A solid backbone made it even heavier. Stones in its stomach ground up the veggie dinners of this early plant-eater.

TRICERATOPS CRETACEOUS
Had a beaky mouth like a parrot to help eat tough vegetation. Who's a pretty polly then?

ANKYLOSAURUS CRETACEOUS
As big as an army tank and covered in bony spikes. Wagged its tail at its enemies and knocked them flying.

VELOCIRAPTOR CRETACEOUS
Sharp teeth and claws like scythes. Probably thought a minute before scratching that itch!

COELOPHYSIS TRIASSIC
These lizard-like creatures were possibly the very first dinosaurs on the Earth.

HOW TO USE YOUR STENCILS

If you have the stencil edition, cut or tear off the stencil sheet from the back of the book. Choose a shape and place it over your paper. Hold it there with masking tape. Draw the outline with pencil or pen. If you have the hardback edition, copy or draw the shapes yourself following the instructions at the front of the book. Use pages 22-23 as a guide to colouring and giving detail to your dinosaurs and pterosaur.

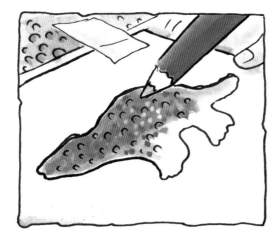

TOP TIP - TOP TIP
Flip over the stencil if you want your dinosaurs fighting each other.

Are you looking at me?

1   Lay the paper over a textured surface to get a scaly skin effect.